Motown Classics
for Keyboard

Music arranged and processed by Barnes Music Engraving Ltd.,
East Sussex TN22 4HA, UK.

Published 1994

IMP

BABY LOVE

Words & Music by Brian Holland, Eddie Holland and Lamont Dozier

Suggested Registration: Electric Piano
Rhythm: Shuffle
Tempo: ♩ = 130

Being With You

Words & Music by William Robinson

Suggested Registration: Jazz Guitar
Rhythm: Soul
Tempo: ♩ = 104

I don't care what they think____ a - bout me, and____

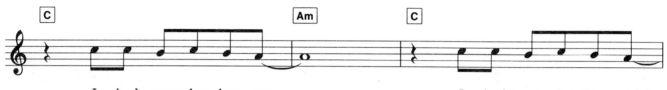

I don't care what they say.____ I don't care what they think,

__ if you're leav-ing, I'm gon-na beg you to stay.__ I don't care if they start

__ to a - void me, I don't care what they do,____ I don't care a-bout a -

- ny-thing else but be-ing with you, be-ing with you. Hon-ey, don't go,____

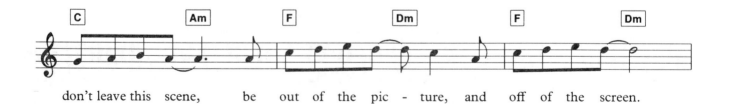

don't leave this scene, be out of the pic - ture, and off of the screen.

BEN

Words by Don Black / Music by Walter Scharf

Suggested Registration: Electric Piano
Rhythm: Soft Rock
Tempo: ♩ = 72

Ben, the two of us need look no more, we both found what we were

look-ing for. With a friend to call my own I'll ne-ver be a-

-lone, and you my friend, will see you've got a friend in me.

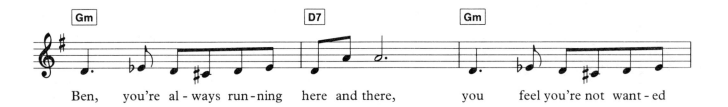

Ben, you're al-ways run-ning here and there, you feel you're not want-ed

a-ny-where. If you ev-er look be-hind, and don't like what you

find, there's some-thing you should know, you've got a place to go.

Dancing In The Street

Words & Music by William Stevenson, Marvin Gaye and Ivy Jo Hunter

Suggested Registration: Saxophone
Rhythm: Rhythm & Blues
Tempo: ♩ = 124

Call - ing out____ a - round____ the world are you rea-dy for a brand new beat?

____ Sum-mer's here, and the time is right for danc-ing in the street.

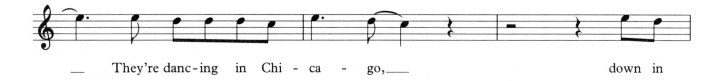

____ They're danc-ing in Chi - ca - go,____ down in

New Or - leans, in New York Ci - ty,____ all we need is mu -

- sic, sweet mu - sic, there'll be mu - sic ev - ery - where,

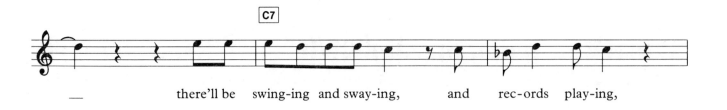

____ there'll be swing-ing and sway-ing, and rec-ords play-ing,

Easy

Words & Music by Lionel Richie

Suggested Registration: Flute
Rhythm: Soft Rock
Tempo: ♩ = 70

Know it sounds fun-ny, but I just can't stand the pain,_

girl I'm leav-ing you___ to - mor - row,____

seems to me girl, you know I've done all_____ I can,

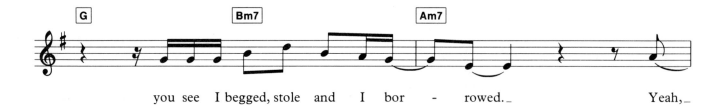

you see I begged, stole and I bor - rowed._ Yeah,_

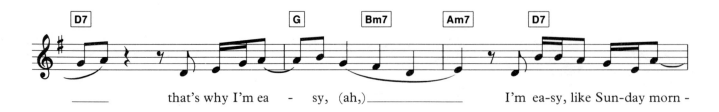

_____ that's why I'm ea - sy, (ah,)_____ I'm ea-sy, like Sun-day morn -

- ing, (ah,)_____ that's why I'm ea - sy, (ah,)_____

For Once In My Life

Words by Ronald Miller / Music by Orlando Murden

Suggested Registration: Electric Piano
Rhythm: 16 Beat
Tempo: ♩ = 112

not like it's hurt me be - fore,____ for once I have some - thing I

know won't de - sert me, I'm not a - lone a - ny - more.____ For

once I can say, this is mine, you can't take it, long as I know I have

love, I can make it, for once in my life I have some-one who needs me._____

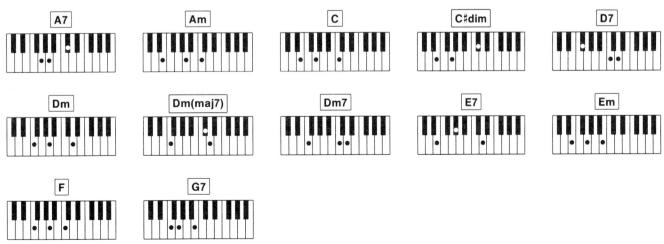

HOW SWEET IT IS
(TO BE LOVED BY YOU)

Words & Music by Eddie Holland, Brian Holland and Lamont Dozier

Suggested Registration: Jazz Organ
Rhythm: Shuffle
Tempo: ♩ = 112

deep - ly touch-es my e - mo - tion.__ I wan-na stop and thank you

ba - by, I wan-na stop and thank you ba - by. Hey now,

__ how sweet it is____ to be loved by you,_ oh ba-by,

how sweet it is____ to be loved by you,_ yes it is.

How sweet it is____ to be loved by you,_ oh ba-by,

how sweet it is____ to be loved by you.

I Heard It Through The Grapevine

Words & Music by Norman Whitfield and Barrett Strong

Suggested Registration: Clarinet
Rhythm: 8 Beat
Tempo: ♩ = 116

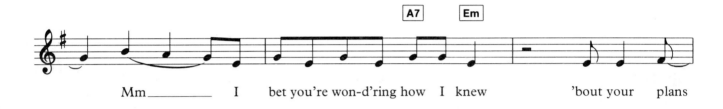

Mm_____ I bet you're won-d'ring how I knew 'bout your plans

_ to make me blue_____ with some oth - er guy_____ you knew be - fore,

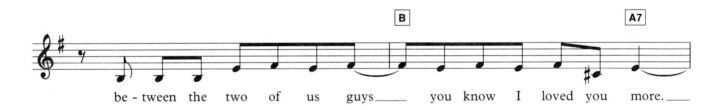

be - tween the two of us guys_____ you know I loved you more._____

_ It took me by sur - prise I must say,_____ when I found

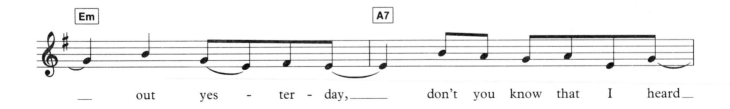

_ out yes - ter - day,_____ don't you know that I heard_

I'll Be There

Words & Music by Berry Gordy, Hal Davis, Willie Hutch and Bob West

Suggested Registration: Flute
Rhythm: Soft Rock
Tempo: ♩ = 92

Lady Marmalade

Words & Music by Bob Crewe and Kenny Nolan

Suggested Registration: Saxophone
Rhythm: Soul
Tempo: ♩ = 116

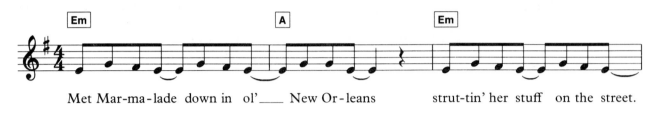

Met Mar-ma-lade down in ol'___ New Or-leans strut-tin' her stuff on the street.

_ She say, 'Hel-lo, hey Joe, you wan-na give it a go___ 'n

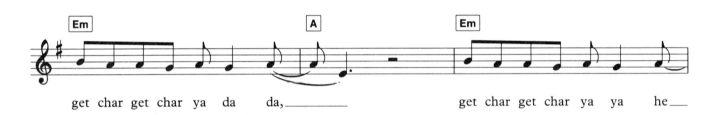

get char get char ya da da,_____ get char get char ya ya he___

_ ya, mo-cha cho-co-la-ta ya___ ya?' Cre-ole La-dy Mar-ma-lade.

'Vou-lez-vous cou-cher a-vec moi,___ ce soir?

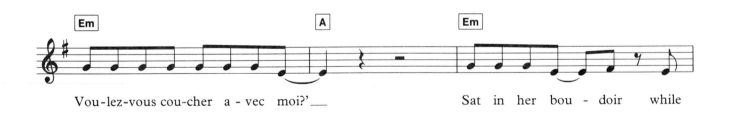

Vou-lez-vous cou-cher a-vec moi?'___ Sat in her bou-doir while

she fresh-ened up, 'n I____ drank her mag - no - lia wine____ up - on her

black sa - tin sheets, I swear I start-ed to freak when she said, 'Get char get char ya da da,___

____ get char get char ya ya he____ ya, mo-cha cho-co - la - ta ya___

__ ya.' Cre-ole La - dy Mar-ma - lade.

'Vou-lez-vous cou-cher a-vec moi,___ ce soir? Vou-lez-vous cou-cher a-vec moi?___

Vou-lez-vous cou-cher a-vec moi,___ ce soir?' Cre-ole La-dy Mar-ma - lade.___

My Guy

Words & Music by William Robinson

Suggested Registration: Saxophone
Rhythm: Pop Swing
Tempo: ♩ = 104

No-thing you could say   could tear____ me a-way   from my____ guy,

no-thing you could do,   'cause I'm stuck   like glue   to my____ guy.

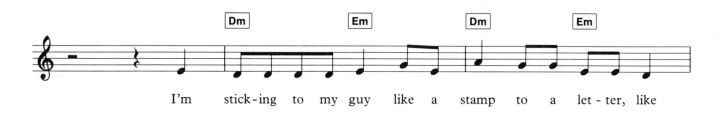

I'm stick-ing to my guy   like a   stamp   to a   let-ter, like

birds   of a fea-ther we   stick to-ge-ther. I'm____ tell-ing you from the start,   I

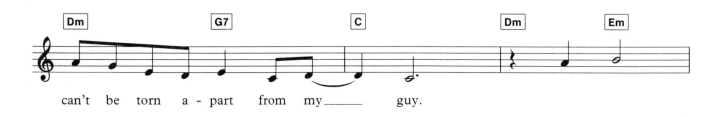

can't   be torn a-part   from my____ guy.

Papa Was A Rollin' Stone

Words & Music by Norman Whitfield and Barrett Strong

Suggested Registration: Muted Trumpet
Rhythm: Rhythm & Blues
Tempo: ♩ = 124

repeat ad lib. for intro.

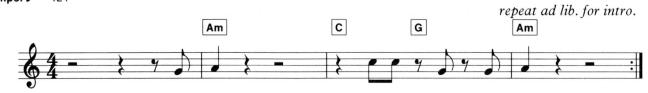

It was the third of Sep-tem - ber,   that day I'll al-ways re - mem -

- ber,___ 'cause that was the day___   that my dad - dy died.___

___   I ne - ver got a chance to see___ him,

ne - ver heard no - thin' but bad___ things a - bout___ him.

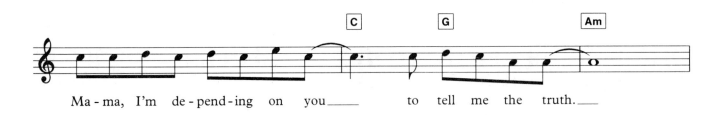

Ma - ma, I'm de - pend-ing on you___ to tell me the truth.___

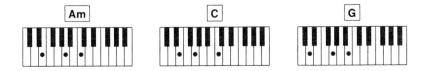

Reach Out, I'll Be There

Words & Music by Brian Holland, Eddie Holland and Lamont Dozier

Suggested Registration: *Jazz Organ*
Rhythm: Soul
Tempo: ♩ = 120

I'll be there___ with a love that will shel-ter you,___

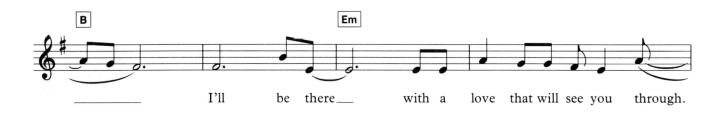

_____ I'll be there___ with a love that will see you through.

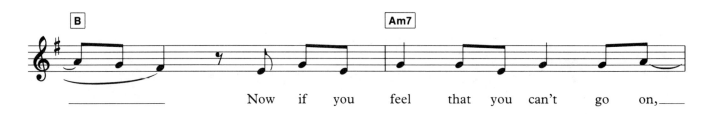

_____ Now if you feel that you can't go on,___

___ be-cause all of your hope is gone,___ and your life___

___ is filled with much con-fu - sion, un - til

hap-pi-ness is just an il-lu - sion, and your world___

STANDING IN THE SHADOWS OF LOVE

Words & Music by Eddie Holland, Lamont Dozier and Brian Holland

Suggested Registration: Saxophone
Rhythm: Rhythm & Blues
Tempo: ♩ = 116

Stand - ing   in   the   sha - dows   of   love,_____   I'm   get - ting

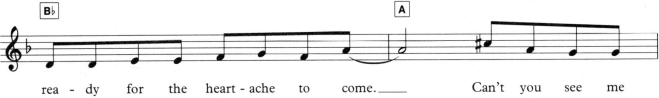

rea - dy   for   the   heart - ache   to   come._____   Can't   you   see   me

stand - ing   in   the   sha - dows   of   love?_____   I'm   get - ting

rea - dy   for   the   heart - aches   to   come. _____

STOP! IN THE NAME OF LOVE

Words & Music by Eddie Holland, Lamont Dozier and Brian Holland

Suggested Registration: Flute
Rhythm: Soul
Tempo: ♩ = 122

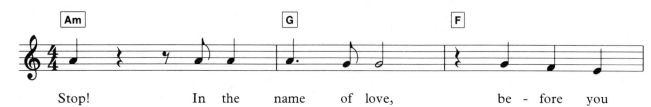

Stop! In the name of love, be - fore you

break my heart.

Ba - by, ba - by I'm a - ware of where you go

each time you leave my door, I watch you walk

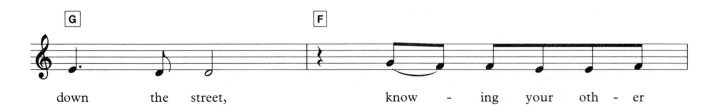

down the street, know - ing your oth - er

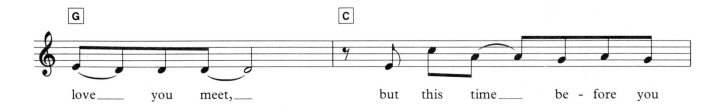

love you meet, but this time be - fore you

THREE TIMES A LADY

Words & Music by Lionel Richie

Suggested Registration: Classical Guitar
Rhythm: Waltz
Tempo: ♩ = 98

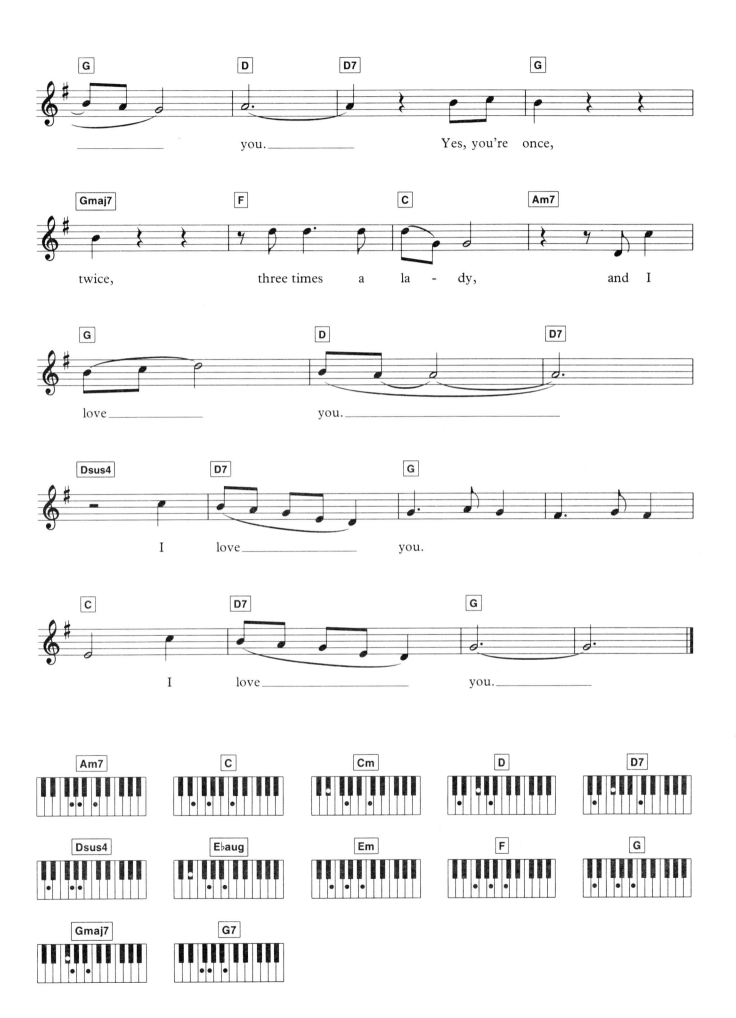

Touch Me In The Morning

Words & Music by Michael Masser and Ronald Miller

Suggested Registration: Electric Piano
Rhythm: Soft Rock
Tempo: ♩ = 72

Touch me in the morn - ing, then just walk a - way.

We don't have to - mor - row, but we had yes - ter - day.

Was - n't it me __ who said that no - thing good's gon - na last for - ev - er?

And was - n't it me __ who said let's just be glad for the time to - ge - ther?

Must - 've been hard to tell me that you've giv - en all __ you had __ to give,

I can un - der - stand your feel - in' that way, __ ev - ery - bo - dy's got __ their life __ to live.

The Tracks Of My Tears

Words & Music by William Robinson, Warren Moore and Marv Tarplin

Suggested Registration: Jazz Organ
Rhythm: 8 Beat
Tempo: ♩ = 104

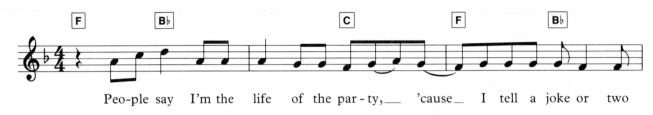

Peo-ple say I'm the life of the par-ty,___ 'cause___ I tell a joke or two

al-though I might be a - laugh - ing loud___ and hear - ty,

deep in - side___ I'm blue. So take a good look at my

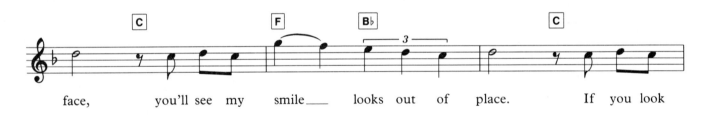

face, you'll see my smile___ looks out of place. If you look

clo - ser it's ea - sy to trace the tracks of my tears. I need

you,___ need___ you. Since you left me, if you

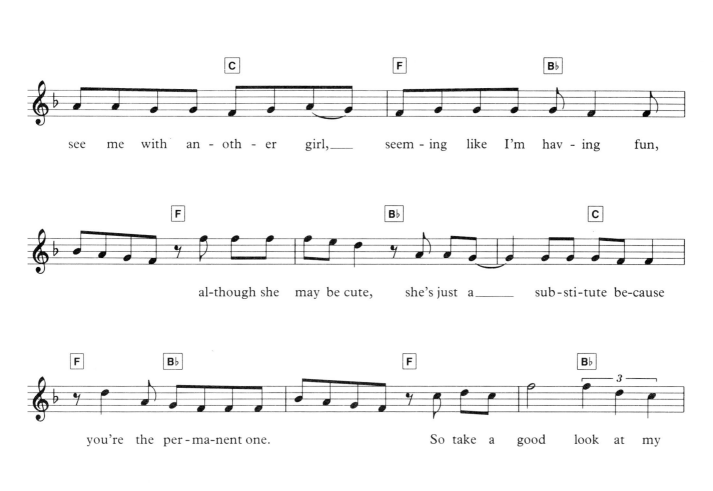

see me with an - oth - er girl,____ seem - ing like I'm hav - ing fun,

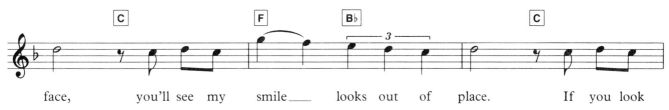

al-though she may be cute, she's just a_____ sub-sti-tute be-cause

you're the per - ma-nent one. So take a good look at my

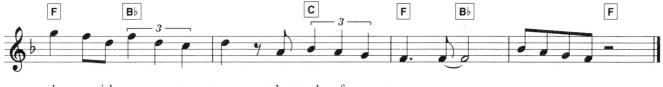

face, you'll see my smile____ looks out of place. If you look

clo - ser it's ea - sy to trace the tracks of my tears.

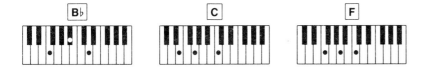

Until You Come Back To Me
(That's What I'm Gonna Do)

Words & Music by Stevie Wonder, Morris Broadnax and Clarence Paul

Suggested Registration: Flute / Pan Pipes
Rhythm: Soft Rock
Tempo: ♩ = 88

Though you don't call a-ny-more, I sit and wait in vain,

I guess I'll rap on your door, tap on your win-dow pane.

I want to tell you ba-by, the chan-ges I've been go-ing through,

miss-ing you, lis-ten you, till you come back to me,

that's what I'm gon-na do. Why did you have to de-cide

you had to set me free? I'm going to

WHAT BECOMES OF THE BROKEN HEARTED

Words & Music by James Dean, Paul Riser and William Weatherspoon

Suggested Registration: Vibraphone
Rhythm: Soft Rock
Tempo: ♩ = 86

As I walk this land with bro-ken dreams, I have vi-sions of ma-ny things,_

love's hap-pi-ness is just an il-lu-sion, filled with sad-ness and con-fu-sion.

What be-comes of the bro-ken heart-ed,_ who had love that's now de-part-ed?

I know I've got to find some kind of peace of mind, may-be.

The fruits of love grow all a-round,_ but for me they come a tum-b-lin' down,_

ev-ery day heart-aches grow a lit-tle strong-er, I can't stand this pain much long-er.

WITH YOU I'M BORN AGAIN

Words & Music by David Shire and Carol Conners

Suggested Registration: Strings
Rhythm: Waltz
Tempo: ♩ = 92

reach - ing through this world in need of one. Come
show me your kind - ness, in your arms I know I'll
find this, ly - ing safe with - in your arms, I'm born a - gain,_____
_____ ly - ing safe with you I'm born a - gain._____

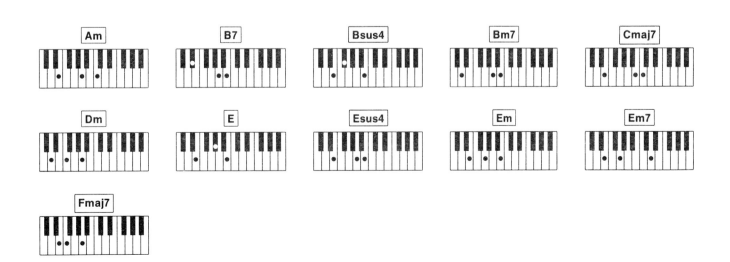

Yester Me, Yester You, Yesterday

Words & Music by Bryan Wells and Ronald Miller

Suggested Registration: Jazz Organ
Rhythm: 8 Beat
Tempo: ♩ = 112

You Can't Hurry Love

Words & Music by Brian Holland, Eddie Holland and Lamont Dozier

Suggested Registration: Vibraphone
Rhythm: 8 Beat
Tempo: ♩ = 92

The Easy Keyboard Library Series

Big Band Hits Order Ref: 19098	**Popular Classics** Order Ref: 4180A
Blues Order Ref: 3477A	**Pub Singalong Collection** Order Ref: 3954A
Celebration Songs Order Ref: 3478A	**Rock 'n' Roll Classics** Order Ref: 2224A
Christmas Carols Order Ref: 4616A	**Traditional Scottish Favourites** Order Ref: 4231A
Christmas Songs Order Ref: 19198	**Showtunes - Volume 1** Order Ref: 19103
Classic Hits - Volume 1 Order Ref: 19099	**Showtunes - Volume 2** Order Ref: 3328A
Classic Hits - Volume 2 Order Ref: 19100	**Soft Rock Collection** Order Ref: 4617A
Country Songs Order Ref: 19101	**Soul Classics** Order Ref: 19201
Traditional English Favourites Order Ref: 4229A	**Summer Collection** Order Ref: 3489A
Favourite Hymns Order Ref: 4179A	**TV Themes** Order Ref: 19196
Film Classics Order Ref: 19197	**The Twenties** Order Ref: 2969A
Great Songwriters Order Ref: 2225A	**The Thirties** Order Ref: 2970A
Instrumental Classics Order Ref: 2338A	**The Forties** Order Ref: 2971A
Traditional Irish Favourites Order Ref: 4230A	**The Fifties** Order Ref: 2972A
Love Songs - Volume 1 Order Ref: 19102	**The Sixties** Order Ref: 2973A
Love Songs - Volume 2 Order Ref: 19199	**The Seventies** Order Ref: 2974A
Music Hall Order Ref: 3329A	**The Eighties** Order Ref: 2975A
Motown Classics Order Ref: 2337A	**The Nineties** Order Ref: 2976A
Number One Hits Order Ref: 19200	**Wartime Collection** Order Ref: 3955A

Wedding Collection
Order Ref: 3688A

Exclusive distributors:

International Music Publications Limited
Southend Road, Woodford Green, Essex IG8 8HN
International Music Publications Limited
25 Rue D'Hauteville, 75010 Paris, France
International Music Publications GmbH Germany
Marstallstrasse 8, D-80539 München, Germany
Nuova Carisch S.R.L.
Via M.F. Quintiliano 40, 20138 Milano, Italy
Danmusik
Vognmagergade 7, DK-1120 Copenhagen K, Denmark